L.O.L. SURPRISE!™

You are invited to this SPECIAL 2022 EDITION

L.O.L. SURPRISE!™
your special ticket

★

Admit One

MIDNIGHT MOVIE

POPCORN

SODA POP

L.O.L. SURPRISE!™
ticket for a friend

★

Admit One

MIDNIGHT MOVIE

LittleBrother
BOOKS

Published 2021. Little Brother Books Ltd, Ground Floor,
23 Southernhay East, Exeter, Devon, EX1 1QL

Printed In Poland. ul. Połczyńska 99,01-303 Warszawa.

books@littlebrotherbooks.co.uk | www.littlebrotherbooks.co.uk

MGA

lolsurprise.com | mgae.com

© MGA

PART 1
Scene selection:

6 Welcome to L.O.Lywood
8 It's a bling thing!
9 Presents, please!
10 Where's Bashful Q.T.?
11 Focus on… Dreamer
12 Super B.B.'s life bustin' tips
14 Go 4 glamour
15 Focus on… Waterfalls
16 Be in Da Band
18 Code cracking with Agent baby and 00L
20 Who's your L.O.L. Surprise! spirit animal?
21 Focus on… Marine Q.T.
22 Sensational edible slime
24 Go for it with Cheer Captain
26 It's a wrap!
27 Focus on… Tough Q.T.
28 Divas with a difference
29 Deck's double up!
30 Weird but true… with Countess!
32 Goin' undercover
33 Focus on… Stomps
34 Be old skool 4 a day with Kansas Q.T.
36 Winter chill doodles!
37 Cozy up for Winter
38 A party to remember with Prom Princess

PART 2
Scene selection:

40 What's your starring role?
41 Focus on… Flipside
42 And the winner is…
44 Chill out
46 #Words Out!
48 Dream design
49 Focus on… Claws
50 No stress allowed
52 Space out!
54 What's your weather vibe?
55 Focus on… Rawr Babe
56 Dance or Dream!
58 Stars in our eyes
60 U complete me!
61 Focus on… Earthy B.B.
62 Magical movie night
64 Bling it out!
65 Focus on… Unity
66 Hangin' on the telephone
68 Shine like a star
70 Hair today
71 Focus on… Sting Girl
72 My life as a movie!
74 Focus on… Star Gazer
75 Say it loud
76 Answers

PROM PRINCESS

© MGA

Welcome to L.O.L.YWOOD

HELLO B.B.
KANSAS QT
SOUL BABE

SCENE 4 | TAKE 2

IT'S LIGHTS, CAMERA, ACTION, AS YOUR FAVOURITE B.B.'S TAKE TO THE CARPET TO STRUT THEIR STUFF.

Get ready for some **big screen** action, starring moments, and some **unforgettable fun!**

Get ready to meet...

BLACK TIE ☐

She's the B.B. host of the L.O.L. awards, and brings the glam to any pink carpet event.

FRINGE EVERYTHING!

AGENT OOL ☐

AGENT BABY ☐

These **super spy** B.B.s are ready to introduce you to some undercover code cracking.

THE GREAT BABY ☐

Soo retro! The Great Baby is all about old skool glamour, with the most up-to-date twist!

IT'S A BLING THING!

SEE HOW MANY FESTIVE WORDS YOU CAN FIT INTO THE GRID.

ACROSS
6. AFTER A HARD DAY THE B.B.S LOVE TO _ _ _ _ _ _ OUT
7. WHAT THE L.O.L.S LOVE AS A GIFT.
8. RUDOLPH PULLS ONE OF THESE.
9. HAPPY _ _ _ _ _ _ _ _ _ TO ONE AND ALL.
10. THEY BRIGHTEN UP THE DARKEST DAY.

DOWN
1. PLAYING THESE PASSES THE TIME ON A COLD WINTER'S DAY.
2. IT DON'T MEAN A THING IF AIN'T GOT THAT _ _ _ _ _.
3. EAT, DRINK AND BE _ _ _ _ _ _.
4. WE DECORATE THESE IN THE HOLIDAY.
5. WE MAKE THESE AT NEW YEAR.
11. THIS WEATHER RHYMES WITH HO, HO HO.

ANSWERS ON p76-77!

PRESENTS, PLEASE!

HOLIDAYS ARE ALL ABOUT GIVING!

Follow the lines to see which present each B.B. receives.

SNOW ANGEL

BIG CITY B.B.

SNOWJAMZ

AWW THANK U FOR MY GIFT!

ANSWERS ON p76-77!

WHO GETS WHAT?

_____ RECEIVES THE GOLD ONE.

_____ RECEIVES THE RED PRESENT.

THAT MEANS _____ RECEIVES THE BLUE GIFT!

© MGA

WHERE'S BASHFUL Q.T.?

She's a shy B.B. that loves to hide!

Can you **pick** out Bashful Q.T. in da crowd?

ANSWERS ON P76-77!

© MGA

FOCUS ON Dreamer

STAR SIGN CAPRICORN 22 DEC TO 19 JAN

STONE RUBY | **LUCKY COLOUR** GREY | **ELEMENT** EARTH

Capricorns like Dreamer think big but keep their feet firmly on the ground. They make **brilliant friends** because they always **think of others** and like to lead by example.

Capricorns never rest until they have everything just **perfect**, whether that's **schoolwork** or **hobbies**.

FABULOUS

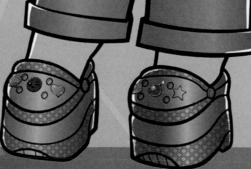

And when it comes to **fashion**, u can be sure that B.B.s like Dreamer have their **signature style** locked down and they step out with **confidence** every time!

SUPER B.B.'S
life bustin' tips

Super B.B. is bursting with **confidence**, but it wasn't always that way! See how she got to be so **totally fabulous**.

GROW, GROW GROW!

Of course you're growing UP. In fact, you're probably growing like crazy. But you've gotta grow from inside, too! Get out of your comfort zone and try something new. Even if it doesn't turn out to be your next best hobby, you will definitely get a lot from shaking off the rut.

NOT EVERYONE GETS IT RIGHT FIRST TIME

Ya think Billie Eilish just woke up one day as an international superstar? Nope! She started small and learned everything she needed to along the way. And that means making a mistake or two… but what's a few mistakes between friends? Learn to embrace your imperfections or better still, style it out, B.B. style!

FEEL THE FEAR… AND DO IT ANYWAY!

This is important. Being afraid is the single most important thing that curbs our confidence. It's NEVER as bad as sitting around thinking about it! Take it from Super B.B.… facing your fears head on is the number one confidence builder!

PUT YOUR BRAIN IN TRAINING. YOU CAN DO IT!

This one's about turning all of those no's into yes we cans! Switch up your mindset to have a can-do 'tude and you'll be amazed at how good you can feel in no time at all!

MAKE YOUR OWN RULES

Life's for livin' right? And that means choosing what's best for you, and not trying to please others! So be good, be kind and be totally, uniquely u!

5 ways to build confidence

- Start a conversation with someone
- Put your hand up in class
- Share your worries
- Try a new skill
- Embarrassing moment? Laugh it off!

GO 4 GLAMOUR

Time for Glamour Queen to hit the pink carpet.

Give **Glamour Queen** a full on sparkle makeover so she's ready for her starring part.

Colour in each award a different shade.

© MGA

FOCUS ON Waterfalls

STAR SIGN AQUARIUS 20 JAN - 18 FEB

STONE GARNET | **LUCKY COLOUR** BLUE | **ELEMENT** AIR

FABULOUS

Waterfalls is a **brilliant BFF** as she knows exactly how to make her **friends feel good.**

She's a true **free spirit** and curious about absolutely everything, so you can be sure you two are gonna have **great adventures together!**

Waterfalls is a **true Aquarius,** she's all about expressing her **creative side,** and letting everyone know all her **cool ideas!**

BE IN DA BAND

STARRING... YOU AND YOUR BESTIES!

CREW MIXTAPE ♡

CREW MIXTAPE ♡

TAKE YOUR PLACE IN THE BAND AND MAKE THE SWEETEST MUSIC EVER!

MAKE YOUR OWN FRIENDSHIP BAND BY PUTTING YOU AND YOUR PALS IN THE STARRING ROLES!

1-2-3-4

THE SINGER - ALTO

IT'S NOT JUST ABOUT HITTING THE RIGHT NOTES. SINGERS LIKE ALTO ALWAYS HAVE THE CROWD'S ATTENTION, AND THEY LOVE TO BE CENTRE STAGE. SURE YOU NEED TALENT, BUT ATTITUDE GOES A LONG WAY, AND SINGERS USUALLY HAVE THAT BY THE BUCKETLOAD.

I WOULD CHOOSE _____

TO BE THE SINGER, BECAUSE _____

_____

PERCUSSION-BHADDIE

THEY KEEP THE BEAT SO THE REST OF THE BAND HAS TIME TO SHINE. BHADDIE LOVES TO ADD HER OWN TWIST TO THE POP CLUB, KNOWING WHEN TO STEP IN AND WHEN TO DIP OUT WITH HER CRASHING CYMBALS. IT'S A SKILL SHE TAKES TO HER FRIENDSHIPS TOO. SHE WILL ALWAYS BE THERE WHEN IT MATTERS.

I WOULD CHOOSE _____

TO SMASH PERCUSSION, BECAUSE _____

_____

GUITAR – RADICAL Q.T.

RADICAL Q.T. KNOWS HOW TO ROCK OUT WITH THE BEST OF THEM, AND SHE'S STILL PARTYING LONG AFTER THE OTHER B.B.S HAVE GONE TO BED. SHE'S A ONE OFF ORIGINAL AND ALWAYS BRINGS SOMETHING DIFFERENT TO THE FRIENDSHIP MIX.

I WOULD CHOOSE _____

TO PLAY GUITAR, BECAUSE _____

_____

1-2-3-4

GRRRL POWER

KEYBOARDS – BANGLE B.B.

THIS B.B. BRINGS A SPRINKLE OF MAGIC TO EVERYTHING SHE DOES, WITH HER CAN-DO ATTITUDE AND HARMONIOUS APPROACH TO LIFE. BANGLE B.B. IS THE ONE WHO ALWAYS KNOWS JUST WHAT TO DO TO GET EVERYONE ELSE GIGGLING AND HAVING A GREAT TIME.

I WOULD CHOOSE _____

TO ROCK THE KEYBOARDS, BECAUSE _____

_____

BACKSTAGE PASS

1-2-3-4

SO THAT'S YOUR BAND! ALL YOU HAVE TO DO NOW IS THINK OF A COOL NAME AND START ROCKING OUT!

17

© MGA

CODE CRACKING

WITH AGENT BABY AND AGENT OOL

The L.O.L. Surprise! dolls always speak it loud and say it proud! Come up with your own slogans for your crew!

LET'S GET CRACKIN'!

BACK TO FRONT
WITH AGENT BABY

All you need to do is turn the **alphabet on its head**. So for A, you would have Z. Fill in all the letters on the grid below, then set your BFF a **challenge** using the **code**!

A B C D E F G H I J K L M

[ ] [ ] [ ] [ ] [ ] [ ] [ ] [ ] [ ] [ ] [ ] [ ] [ ]

N O P Q R S T U V W X Y Z

[ ] [ ] [ ] [ ] [ ] [ ] [ ] [ ] [ ] [ ] C B A

MAKE YOUR OWN
TOTALLY CRAZY CODE

This one is going to take some thought between **you** and **your BFF**. It's a strictly **no-writing code**! Instead, you can use hand signals, blinks, jumps or claps to tell your friend how you're **feeling**.

HAVE A GO AT FILLING IN YOUR OWN SECRET CODE GESTURES HERE.

meaning:	gesture:
HELLO	TWO BLINKS
FEELIN' GOOD	
CALL ME LATER	
YOU'RE SO FUNNY	
BFS FOREVER	

Some BBFs like to work a **numbers only** policy with their **secret messaging**. So give this numbers code a try and be a cool 10, every time! Use a **number** for each letter of the alphabet.

EXCITED YET?

A = 1	H =	O =	V =
B = 2	I =	P =	W =
C = 3	J =	Q =	X =
D =	K =	R =	Y =
E =	L =	S =	Z =
F =	M =	T =	
G =	N =	U =	

A SECRET CODE FOR MY BFF

Who's your *L.O.L. Surprise!* SPIRIT ANIMAL?

TIME TO CHOOSE YOUR FOREVER FUR BALL!

Get ready for your perfect pet reveal

All you need to do is **stare** at the whole page for ten seconds. **Close your eyes**, then open them. The first pet that jumps out to you is your L.O.L. **spirit animal!**

IT KITTY

BRRRD

DOLLMATIAN

SNOW BUNNY

SHOWPONY

BUNNY CHAMP

POSH PUP

ROLLER KITTY 10

HOP HOP SPRINTS

ROLLS

COZY KITTY

ROYAL KITTY-CAT

MY SPIRIT ANIMAL IS _____

FOCUS ON Marine Q.T.

STAR SIGN **PISCES** 19 FEB TO 20 MARCH

STONE AMETHYST | **LUCKY COLOUR** SEA GREEN | **ELEMENT** WATER

Marine is a **creative whirlwind**, full of artistic ideas and brave enough to try them all out.

Marine is one **daydreaming B.B.** and that's what makes her so **special!**

Pisces like Marine make brilliant best friends as they are **great listeners** and are always sensitive to others' feelings.

RARE

You can count on a Pisces to keep **calm** in a friendship crisis, and above all their **dreamy nature** means you'll always have **lots of fun**.

21

© MGA

Sensational EDIBLE SLIME

YOU'VE MADE IT BEFORE... BUT DID YOU KNOW YOU CAN MAKE **SLIME** THAT **TASTES YUMMY** TOO?

YOU WILL NEED

❄ Microwave
❄ Microwaveable bowl
❄ Metal spoons

INGREDIENTS

❄ 1 cup of gummies
❄ 2 tablespoons icing sugar
❄ 2 tablespoons cornflower
❄ 1 teaspoon coconut oil, optional

1

METHOD:

Heat the gummies in the microwave for 10-15 seconds. **Be careful**, the gummies may be hot. Take the bowl out and stir the gummies. Put them in for a few more seconds if you need to, until their **shape starts to melt**.

2

Stir the gummies, then gradually **fold in** the icing sugar and cornstarch in equal amounts. the gummies will soon form a **slime consistency!**

3

You can **eat it straight away** or you can play around with the **consistency**. If you add a little more corn flour or icing sugar, the slime will become thicker.

TIP
If you want it to be **stretchier** add a little coconut oil.

SO FUN SOOO YUM!

GO FOR IT
with Cheer Captain

LEARN TO LAUGH

Ok, so it's definitely embarrassing when you call the teacher 'Mum' by accident... so cringe! But even if your face is red as a beetroot, giggling at silly mistakes will make them disappear. And if it happens again? Just style it out!

POP CORN

TAKE IT OUT OF THE COMFORT ZONE

No one ever got to win a gold medal without leaving the starting blocks! So don't be afraid to try new things, even if you don't get it right first time. Cool B.B.s know that feeling confident comes from challenging yourself.

CELEBRATE THE LITTLE THINGS

Whether you aced the test, were commended by the teacher or even learned to tie your own laces, build yourself up, you deserve it! Little achievements can spur you on to be bolder next time. Cheer Captain has your back on this one!

Cheer Captain was **born confident**, but that doesn't mean we all are! Take some tips from her to feel **good and go 4 it**.

SET YOURSELF GOALS

Rome wasn't built in a day and neither were your dreams! You gotta break it down into bite sized chunks! Writing down goals will help you see that even small things are a big achievement, and it should spur you on to greater success.

KEEP THE BIG PICTURE IN MIND

Confidence is kinda like a snowball… it starts small and ends up enormous! Start taking some little steps and you'll soon see your confidence grow. And if you can share your wins with a friend like Cheer Captain, you'll know that your friend has your back on this one, too!

IT'S A WRAP!

BIG CITY B.B. NEEDS SNOW ANGEL'S HELP WITH SOME HOLIDAY PREP!

Help Big City B.B. **pick up** all the decorations, then find **Snow Angel**.

START

FINISH!

ANSWERS ON p76-77!

© MGA

FOCUS ON Tough Q.T.

STAR SIGN ARIES 21 MARCH TO 19 APRIL

STONE DIAMOND	LUCKY COLOUR RED	ELEMENT FIRE

Aries like Q.T. **love their friends** above everything else, and place them amongst the most **important people** in their lives.

Like most Aries, Tough Q.T. is **straight from the heart** and leaps into life full of energy for the **day ahead!**

FABULOUS

Tough Q.T. can take any situation in hand and loves to **lead the way** when it comes to friendships.

You'll definitely feel **loved** if you're friends with an Aries! Generous, confident and honest, you can be sure to rely on Tough Q.T. to always **have your back.**

DIVAS WITH A DIFFERENCE!

THE B.B.'S ARE TAKING DANCE ROUTINES TO DA NEXT LEVEL!

POWER UP!

Colour an emoji each time you spot a difference between the two pictures.

DECKS DOUBLE UP!

Draw circles around the two tape decks that match.

A

B

C

D

E

LETS DANCE!

ANSWERS ON p76-77!

GOIN' UNDERCOVER

COLOUR THE DOTS TO BRING THESE B.B.S TO LIFE

AGENT OOL

AGENT BABY

FOCUS ON Stomps

STAR SIGN TAURUS 20 APRIL TO 20 MAY

STONE **EMERALD** LUCKY COLOUR **GREEN** ELEMENT **EARTH**

Stomps is a great name for a Taurus. It's the sign of the **bull** and while they can be **stubborn and fierce**, there's a gentle and caring side to them that makes them a **fantastic friend**.

Stomps likes all the **good things** in life and her favourite thing to do above all is **chill**!

FABULOUS

Taureans spend a lot of time **thinking about things** before they make a decision and that's why they have a hard time changing their mind when they've **made a decision**.

BE OLD SKOOL 4 A DAY
with Kansas Q.T.

Can u imagine life without devices? No phones, tablets or Wi Fi could be great fun for a little while at least! Kansas Q.T. is all about living olden days lyfe!

See **how many** of these old skool **challenges** you can complete.

CHAT IRL

IRL means **in real life**, and there's no better way to experience that than by spending time with people you like. Having fun hanging out is so much better done **face to face**. It's just not the same on video, let's 'face' it!

I SPENT TIME WITH A FRIEND.

GET OLD SCHOOL
WITH PENS AND PENCILS

Time to unleash your creativity! Without any distractions you can totally lose yourself in your imagination and create something really cool! Try painting a portrait of a friend, or if painting's not your thing, try sewing or crafts.

I GOT BUSY WITH MY ART SUPPLIES.

TURN OFF YOUR PHONE
OR TABLET

Ok, so this going to be the **challenge of all challenges**. But think of all the time you'll get back in the day without messages, photos and videos.

I TURNED MY PHONE OFF.

GET OUTSIDE!

Sure, everyone says this is what they want kids to do, but you know it does kinda feel good! Feeling the **sunshine**, bouncing on a trampoline, running, jumping… there just isn't anything better, especially if you're with your **top B.B.s**!

I RAN, JUMPED AND PLAYED WITH THE BEST OF 'EM!

LIKE TOTES ANALOGUE!

WRITE A LETTER

Wow, can you believe this is what people used to do before computers were invented? Writing a letter to someone is actually a really great way to show them that they're special. And best of all, you might even get a reply in return!

I PENNED A NOTE TO A PAL.

35

WINTER CHILL
DOODLES!

Use **ice-cool** blues and **pinks** for this snowy scene!

GLITTERALLY DREAMING

MISS SNOW

L.O.L. SURPRISE!

COZY UP FOR WINTER

When it's cold outside...
make like Snow Leopard.

HAVE A PJ DAY

No one needs to be asked twice for this one! Having a whole day in your favourite onesie is the **ultimate** in **chill**. Just ask Prezzie... her off duty comfy look is so totally **B.B.-li-zzz-ious**!

JUST CHILL OUT!

Snow Leopard knows that when the weather stops you from having fun, it's just it's way of telling you to **slow down**! You don't have to be anywhere or do anything. **Take chill** to the next level and enjoy a whole day of nothingness!

GO SLOW

Make the most of the **little things** that make a day **super special**! Plan to make the ultimate hot chocolates with sprinkles and marshmallows, then snuggle up watching your **favourite movie**.

MAKEOVER YOUR CHILL SPACE

We're taking duvets, pillows, blankets... everything you can grab to make your room the ultimate **cosy palace**! Don't forget fairy lights, LEDS and of course, some **midnight feast snacks**!

AND THE WINNER IS...

ALL OF YOUR FRIENDS ARE OSCAR-WORTHY.

Write the names of one of your BFFs on each of these L.O.L. Surprise! Awards.

POPCORN

SODA POP

FOR BEING THE QUEEN OF FUN!

....

FOR THROWING KINDNESS AROUND LIKE CONFETTI!

....

FOR BEING THE SMARTEST COOKIE EVER!

....

FOR ALWAYS CHEERING EVERYONE ELSE ON! GO GIRL!

....

FOR ALWAYS KNOWING THE LATEST DANCES!

....

MAKE UP YOUR OWN AWARD HERE:

FOR
....

....

43

DREAM DESIGN

Create a roarsome outfit for
Snow Leopard right here, right now.

© MGA

FOCUS ON Claws

STAR SIGN CANCER 21 JUNE TO 22 JULY

STONE MOONSTONE | **LUCKY COLOUR** SILVER | **ELEMENT** WATER

FABULOUS

Cancer girls like Claws can always be **relied on** to take care of their friends and family. happy because they know that they can always depend on you, no matter what.

Everyone knows they can **depend on Claws**, no matter what. No wonder everybody loves a Cancer girl!.

Claws is generous, **endlessly kind** and **super-loving**. Her Cancer-side means she loves pets too. Just ask Claws about her crab!

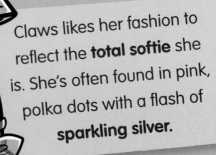

Claws likes her fashion to reflect the **total softie** she is. She's often found in pink, polka dots with a flash of **sparkling silver**.

No STRESS allowed

YOU'RE GONNA LOVE SQUEEZING YOUR NEW BEST FRIEND: AN EASY-PEASY-TO-MAKE SQUISHY STRESS BALL!

YOU WILL NEED:

- **3 balloons** ☐
- Rice or flour ☐
- **Funnel** ☐
- Safety scissors ☐

Younger readers should always ask a grown-up for help

BALLOONS

SURPRISE TIP!

If you want some extra stretch: simply blow up your balloon first. (Don't forget to let the air out again!)

1 Stretch out your balloon!

RICE

FLOUR

FLOUR

2 Choose your filling. Rice or flour. Either is good!

3 Stick your funnel into the neck of the balloon.

4 Now slowly fill the balloon. Make sure you pour slowly to avoid clogging the neck of your balloon.

5 Remove the funnel from the balloon and let out as much air as you can.

6 Tie the neck of the balloon closed tightly.

7 Carefully snip off the excess rubber.

8 Grab your second balloon and snip off the end, then stuff your first balloon into it. Tie the end of the balloon.

9 Reach for your third balloon, and stuff your other balloon into it.

10 Tie the end, and hurrah! You've made yourself a squishy stress ball aka your new BFF!

LOOK AFTER YOURSELF!

IF YOU WANT TO GET SUPER-CREATIVE, DRAW A FACE ON YOUR SQUISHY BALL.

IT WILL MAKE YOU SMILE WHENEVER YOU WANT TO LOOK AT IT!

SPACE OUT!

ARE YOU READY FOR SOME SCI-FI GIGGLES WITH GLAMSTRONAUT? READY? STEADY? LOL!

IT'S STORY TIME . . .

Complete the list below, then **fill in** the **blanks** on the **opposite page** with the words you came up with.

There's no right or wrong answer. Just write whatever comes into your head!

1 **A name** ....

2 **Your fave celeb** ....

3 **Another celeb** ....

4 **A number** ....

5 **A vegetable** ....

6 **A fruit** ....

7 **An animal** ....

8 **A made up word** ....

9 **A game** ....

10 **An adjective** ....

I flew into **space** with another **astronaut** called **1** ....

and **Glamstronaut**. Suddenly we got a call from **2** ....

.... who had just landed on **Planet L.O.L.** with

3 .... They had met **4** ....

super-sweet aliens who were the colour of a **5** ....

smelt of a **6** .... and looked a little like

a **7** .... **Wowzas!**

1 .... and **2** .... were

thinking of naming them **8** .... They wanted us to

meet them. Glamstronaut and I **zoomed** straight over in our rocket. We met

the **8** ....

They were super-nice. We all played **9** ....

together. You could say it was a **10** ....

outta this world adventure!

THE END

What's your WEATHER VIBE?

Find out if you're a ray of sunshine or super cool...

Start

What do you wear to a fancy dress party?

→ SOMETHING FUNNY → **You pride yourself on making friends crack up!**

↓ SOMETHING STYLISH

Your friend wants to go rock-climbing. You:

→ GIVE IT A GO → **Your mate gets a karaoke game for her birthday. You:**

↓ SUGGEST NETFLIX INSTEAD

At a party, you:

→ HIT THE DANCE FLOOR

↓ HIT THE BUFFET

You pride yourself on making friends crack up!

→ ALWAYS → **You fall over in public. You:**

↓ NOT ME

You fall over in public. You:

RUN AND HIDE

CAN'T STOP LAUGHING →

Your mate gets a karaoke game for her birthday. You:

BELT OUT YOUR FAVE SONG → **Your pal's down in the dumps. You:**

↓ PRETEND TO LOSE YOUR VOICE

Your pal's down in the dumps. You:

AVOID HER

CHEER HER UP ↓

At a sleepover, are you always the last one to doze off?

→ YES → **Someone suggests a dance-off. You:**

↓ NO

JUDGE IT

TAKE PART

SUPER-COOL

You're **totes level-headed like Bashful Q.T**. Make sure you're **not** missing out on any hilarious **bud-bonding** opportunities. Don't worry about looking silly, that's part of the **fun**.

BREATH OF FRESH AIR

Like On Pointe you **love** to kick back and have a **good time**, but you also know to dial back the **craziness** when it's time to deal with schoolwork or **friend** drama.

RAY OF SUNSHINE

Fun is your middle name. You and Bold B.B. **super-spontaneous** and don't see the point of taking yourself too seriously. No wonder **everyone loves** having you around.

Rawr Babe

STAR SIGN LEO 23 JULY TO 22 AUGUST

STONE TOURMALINE | **LUCKY COLOUR ORANGE** | **ELEMENT FIRE**

Leo girls like Rawr Babe are natural **leaders**, so you're already making a big impact at school.

Leos are definitely not scared of hard work, especially when it leads you to all the **good** stuff.

Just like **Rawr Babe**, you're doing well at your favourite subjects and have a **good idea** of what you want to be later on.

FABULOUS

Both you and Rawr Babe are **lively**, totally fashion forward and love **excitement** so expect the unexpected over the next few years!

DANCE or DREAM!

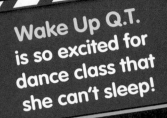

Wake Up Q.T. is so excited for dance class that she can't sleep!

I'M SO EXCITED!

There is a dance class tomorrow and Wake Up Q.T. can't wait to dance her heart out. "The sooner, I go to sleep, the sooner tomorrow will come!" she says, changing into her night clothes.

NAP TIME

TOTALLY YUMMY!

Wake up Q.T. snuggles up in bed. She pulls her sleep mask over her eyes and tries to drift off. But it's no good. "I'm too excited to sleep!" Wake Up Q.T. sighs.

Wake Up Q.T. tries counting minis, but she's still wide awake. "Maybe something in my tummy will help!" Wake Up Q.T. heads into the kitchen and makes a gigantic sandwich.

SO MANY CLOTHES, SO LITTLE TIME!

WERK IT!

Even after her snack, Wake Up Q.T. isn't tired. She sorts through her wardrobe to find the perfect dance outfit. "If I go to bed now, I should still get enough sleep!" she says.

Sleep just won't come. "Perhaps a workout will make me sleep!" she says. Wake Up Q.T. steps and jumps until she's totally puffed out. But she's still not tired.

Wake Up Q.T. tries singing, but just wakes up Ruff Rover. "You know what?" She says. "I"m just too tired to sleep. I'm going to stay awake all night instead!"

She lies down on her sofa. Without meaning to, Wake Up Q.T. doses off. Hours later, she wakes up. "Oh no!" she cries, looking at the time. "I'm late for class!"

Wake Up Q.T. rushes to the studio. The dance class has started. "I'm sorry I'm late!" gasps Wake Up Q.T. "You'll just have to try and catch up!" Says Phenom

Phenom B.B. hits the lights so the friends can practise their black light discodancing. "Oh no! That's making me sleepy!" yawns Wake Up Q.T.

She sits down and immediately falls asleep, missing the rest of the dance class. She only wakes up when her friends jump in the pool, splashing water all over her.

"Wow!" says Wake Up Q.T. noticing her clothes are soaked. "I must really have worked up a sweat in that dance class!" She waves goodbye to all her friends.

THE END!

© MGA

Stars in our eyes

WANNA KNOW WHAT SURPRISES THE YEAR'S GOT AHEAD? WITCHY BABE'S GOT YOU COVERED!

CAPRICORN

22 Dec – 19 Jan

If there's a goal you want to reach, **write it down.** Then work out the steps you need to get there.

Good fortune is shining on you!

Your surprise charm: Squishie

AQUARIUS

20 Jan – 18 Feb

You're going to be the voice of reason in **your friendship group.** So take a deep breath and tell everyone what you really think.

You'll be so **pleased** you did!

Your surprise charm: Daisy ring

PISCES

19 Feb – 20 Mar

Things that have been confusing you **will start to fall into place.** Use your new knowledge to make things better. Having **patience** will be key!

Your surprise charm: Stripy socks

ARIES

21 Mar – 19 Apr

Tell someone you trust what's been **bothering you.** It'll make you feel so much better. Plus you'll get some **awesome advice** back and grow even closer!

Your surprise charm: Toy cat

TAURUS

20 Apr – 20 May

You'll get the chance to let your hair down and **let yourself go.** Enjoy every minute, you're about to create some extra **special memories**.

Your surprise charm: Slogan t-shirt

© MGA

GEMINI

21 May – 20 Jun

You're totally heading for the spotlight. So go for it and do something super daring. Applause will definitely follow. So **go for it!**
Your surprise charm: Red shoes

CANCER

21 Jun – 22 Jul

Something you've been looking forward to may not go to plan, but something amazing will come out of it. **Good things** come to those who wait.
Your surprise charm: Heart key ring

LEO

23 Jul – 22 Aug

Make sure you're open to meeting new friends, as an awesome new lifelong BFF-ship could totally be on the cards. **How exciting!**
Your surprise charm: Glitter pen

VIRGO

23 Aug – 22 Sept

Keep in mind that anything worth having is going to take a bit of work. Get ready to put some serious graft in.
A **big surprise** is heading your way!
Your surprise charm: Gold necklace

LIBRA

23 Sept – 22 Oct

Make sure you pay attention to the little things. A friend will be looking to **share a secret** with you. It's a good one so don't give in to the urge to blab.
Your surprise charm:
Lockable diary

SCORPIO

23 Oct – 21 Nov

A little quiet could do you good. Make some time to chill out at home in front of Netflix with a big bowl of popcorn. **Big things** are coming your way.
Your surprise charm: Heart sunglasses

SAGITTARIUS

22 Nov – 21 Dec

You've got a great idea, but aren't sure how to make it happen. Talk it out with your friends and family. Many hands will make light work, and the **rewards** are so worth it!
Your surprise charm: Scented eraser

© MGA

U COMPLETE ME!

Let your inner style guru run free! Finish this drawing of Bold B.B. Make her fabulous!

Colour her in to add that extra **glamour!**

© MGA

FOCUS ON Earthy B.B.

STAR SIGN VIRGO 23 AUGUST TO 22 SEPT

STONE SAPPHIRE | **LUCKY COLOUR GREEN** | **ELEMENT EARTH**

You and Earthy B.B. are **gentle, super-organised** and a little on the **shy** side.

Both you and Earthy B.B. are very **choosy** when it comes to your BFFs and life in general, but only because **you know who you are** and what you want.

You do **brilliantly** at school 'cos you always strive to do your best. You're happier taking a back seat and **helping your friends** to shine.

FABULOUS

Your friends adore you, and that Virgo charm of yours will get you absolutely **anywhere you wanna go!**

61

© MGA

Magical MOVIE NIGHT

7 seriously cool ways to create a **night** to **remember!**

PRODUCTION — HELLO B.B.
DIRECTOR — KANSAS QT
CAMERA — SOUL BABE
DATE 8/2 | SCENE 4 | TAKE 2

POP THAT CORN!

Get ready to concoct the next **flavour** sensation! **Sprinkle** in anything from M&Ms and marshmallows to peanut butter or paprika. The sky's the limit (or whatever's **in the cupboard** anyway!)

GET COOKING

Create a **meal** around the movie you're watching. Banana splits would be **super fun** if you're watching The Jungle Book, or crack out the cheese if you're **giggling** through Tom and Jerry.

CRAZY COMPETITION

Pick a few actions or catch phrases from the movie you're about to watch and **base a game** on them. The first one to call it when the actions or catchphrase happens gets to create a **dare** for the rest of the room. They could do 10 jumping jacks or not be allowed to say yes or no for the rest of the night!

PLAY DRESS UP

Everything is more fun when you've got a costume on. Make everyone **dress as a character** in the movie or create a theme. You can all be **super heroes** if you're settling down for *Space Jam: A New Legacy* or **princesses** if you're having a *Frozen* night.

SUPER SEATING

Grab some cardboard boxes and **get creative** with the seating. With a few snips, some markers and tape you can turn a basic box into a spaceship, a car or a castle. Perfect to **snuggle** inside.

DON'T JUST WATCH!

Get up and **dance** to the music, practice your swing if you're watching a baseball movie or take it in turns to pretend the remote is a mic if anyone **breaks into song.**

HOME CINEMA

Turn your house into the best cinema ever. Print out **tickets** and show everyone to their assigned seating for the movie. Load **gift bags** with sweets, drinks and popcorn and give them out. So cool!

63

BLING IT OUT!

UNBOX A LIL JOY AND FIND ALL THE BLING INSPIRED WORDS IN THE GRID.

Look **across, down** and **diagonally**

Y	Y	H	L	T	I	E	E	W	O	L	G
B	R	O	U	S	E	D	L	A	C	J	H
G	R	L	L	S	E	A	S	O	N	C	R
F	E	I	L	I	O	V	I	T	S	L	I
I	M	D	I	O	G	V	L	U	N	S	D
E	E	A	H	F	T	N	R	C	P	O	S
R	L	Y	C	R	X	P	I	A	R	L	U
C	F	S	O	O	R	U	R	L	E	C	O
E	I	I	B	I	H	K	S	I	B	I	J
Y	E	N	S	D	L	O	G	T	C	I	Q
E	U	E	M	E	J	H	H	U	H	B	W

TICK THESE WORDS OFF AS YOU FIND THEM.

Glow ☐	Bling ☐	Chill ☐	Elfie ☐
Sparkle ☐	Surprise ☐	Merry ☐	Holidays ☐
Fierce ☐	Sleigh ☐	Season ☐	Unbox ☐

ANSWERS ON p76-77!

FOCUS ON Unity

STAR SIGN LIBRA 23 SEPT TO 22 OCTOBER

STONE OPAL | **LUCKY COLOUR PINK** | **ELEMENT AIR**

You and Unity are friendly, caring and **super attentive**.

RARE

You're at your happiest when you're surrounded by lots of other people, having lots of **fun** and **giggles**.

Being the sign of the scales, you're brilliant at weighing things up, which means you make **excellent choices** at school and are the one in the gang who can be **counted** on to sort out any arguments.

Just like Unity, your friends will always turn to you for your **straight talkin' advice**. They know you'll always be there for them no matter where you are or what's going on.

HANGIN' ON THE TELEPHONE

A   **B**   **C**

SUPER SELFIE

Oops. Something's gone wrong with Fierce's photo app. Can you see who's in which photo?

1 **2** **3**

DRAW LINES FROM EACH PHOTO TO THE RIGHT OPENING ACT MEMBER.

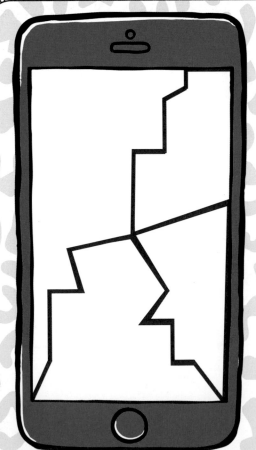

IN BITS

The Hairflipz are having a clumsy day! Now Bluegrass Queen has smashed her phone screen. Draw lines to put the pieces back in the correct place.

1

2   **3**   **4**

ANSWERS ON p76-77!

WE'VE GOT YOUR NUMBER!

Pick a number from Rebel's phone to see what it reveals about you.

Shut your eyes and hover your index over the phone numbers. Drop your finger, then read to see what that number says about you!

IF YOU LANDED ON:

0 No one can resist you with your infectious laugh and high spirts.

1 Your style is always picture-perfect. The more sparkles the better!

2 You're a true superhero, saving the world one green act at a time!

3 Your artistic nature shines through in every single thing that you do!

4 You love interacting with others. Team work makes the dream work!

5 You can analyse any problem, and always find a way to solve it!

6 You're super-confident and love being the centre of attention.

7 With your easy style and sense of humour, you make everyone happy.

8 Shop 'til you drop is your motto! So many shops and so little time!

9 When it comes to big hearts, yours is ginormous. You generous thing, you!

SHINE LIKE A STAR

STEP INTO THE LIMELIGHT WITH GLAMOUR QUEEN'S STEP-BY-STEP GUIDE.

BE YOU

Learning to be yourself is awesome. There's no one better than you. You rock. Don't ever forget it.

Find your inner voice: **Shout how awesome you are from the rooftops!**

BE DIFFERENT

Standing out from the crowd is a good thing, as Glamour Queen knows. Let your personality shine through wherever you are.

Find your inner star: **Always be true to yourself**

SHOW OFF

It's good to have things you're proud of. Sometimes you just gotta swag it out. Display your art or school reports right now!

Find your inner star: **Don't be afraid to say what you're good at.**

BEST ACTION B.B.

DRESS UP

Jewellery is a simple way to make you feel fab. Layer on your fave necklaces or bracelets to feel instantly star-licious.

Find your inner star: Repeat after us:
It's the little things that count!

GET CONFIDENT

Even the most confident stars worry sometimes. You've gotta fake it til you make it. So hold your head up high and smile.

Find your inner star:
Tell that inner critic to take a hike!

STAR SCRIBBLES

Every star needs a stand out **signature**.
Get practising yours here:

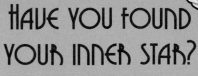

HAVE YOU FOUND YOUR INNER STAR?

Tick three statements you agree with...

You always look on the bright side

You love your own company

You're not good at sharing your feelings

You never ever give up

You act before you think

You can keep a secret

SO HOW DID YOU DO?

MOSTLY PINK

You follow your dreams and give everything your best shot. Your never-give up 'tude means you work hard to achieve your dreams.

MOSTLY BLUE

You ooze confidence but inside you're not always so sure. You always put others ahead of yourself, no wonder everyone thinks you're a star already!

HAIR TODAY

WHICH HAIR-MAZING STYLE SHOULD YOU TRY NEXT?

CIRCLE THE ANSWERS THAT BEST FIT YOUR STYLE.

MY STYLE IS
- **A** Girly
- **B** So fashion
- **C** Casual

I LOVE
- **A** Acting
- **B** Writing
- **C** Activities

I LOVE ANYTHING
- **A** Comfy
- **B** Trendy
- **C** Sporty

MY FRIENDS SAY I'M
- **A** Shy
- **B** Creative
- **C** Energetic

MY FAVE ACCESSORY IS MY
- **A** Friends
- **B** Kindle
- **C** Trainers

SO WHAT HAIRSTYLE SHOULD YOU TRY? IF YOU ANSWERED MOSTLY...

A

BRAID IT LIKE NAE NAE

You can be on the shy side, but when you walk out with these braids all your nerves will magically drop away.

B

BOW-A-LICIOUS LIKE ALTO

You love nothing better than getting creative and trying out the latest styles. Blaze a trail with a head-turning bow.

C

PONY IT UP LIKE SOPRANO

Your sporty nature and boundless energy means you want to brush and go. This style would suit you down to the ground.

70

Sting Girl

STAR SIGN SCORPIO 23 OCTOBER TO 21 NOVEMBER

STONE AQUAMARINE | **LUCKY COLOUR BLACK** | **ELEMENT WATER**

Look out world! Sting Girl is a Scorpio and has a very **strong personality!**

Scorpios like Sting Girl are **warm, affectionate** and not afraid to go after what they want.

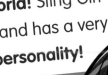

This doll is **trustworthy**, hates wasting time and is a **natural-born leader.**

FABULOUS

Sting Girl is close to her family and has a **large group of friends,** She still **needs her own space** though, and as long as everyone respects that, she's happy.

Sting Girl knows how to turn on that endless charm of hers, and can **twist pretty much anyone around her little finger** with just a flash of that smile!

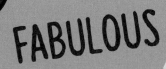

MY LIFE AS A MOVIE!

LIGHTS...CAMERA... ACTION...TIME TO MAKE YOUR OWN FILM...

BFF S.O.S.

It's hard to make movie magic on your own. Call your friends and get them involved. For a quick, short movie, you can get everyone together and shoot something in a single day. Hurrah!

PLAN AHEAD

Don't panic, you don't need to have a script or a storyboard or anything professional that take ages. Scribble down a general story or a list of shots or at the very least have the ending sussed before you begin.

GADGETS A GO GO!

Framing, telling a story, good shots and editing can all be done on the simplest camera including the camera on a phone or tablet. So the good news is you probably have everything you need already!

EXCELLENT EDITING

If you like laughing, editing makes the jokes punchier. If you like action, editing makes it more exciting. Every type of film needs editing and there's loads of free software to help you do it. Dive in and play around.

BEHIND THE SCENES

Clips that let you go behind the scenes are not only fun, but help you learn loads. Don't worry if you make mistakes in your movie, even Hollywood makes mistakes too and have to reshoot whole scenes.

KEEP GOING

Keep at it, have fun and you'll get better and better at making movies. When you have your first movie 'in the can' have a screening at your house. YOU'VE MADE IT! CONGRATS!

Draw a poster for your movie here...

HELLO B.B.
PRODUCTION   KANSAS QT
DIRECTOR   SOUL BABE
CAMERA
DATE   SCENE   TAKE
8/2   4   2

FOCUS ON StarGazer

STAR SIGN SAGITTARIUS 22 NOV TO 21 DEC

STONE TURQUOISE   **LUCKY COLOUR** PURPLE   **ELEMENT** FIRE

RARE

Star Gazer is **confident, creative** and always looks on the bright side of life!

Star Gazer loves nothing better than a good, old **debate**, and is always happy to **speak up in class** whether she knows the answer or not!

People enjoy being around this girl, because she's **honest** and loves trying out new things.

This doll loves being around others and as a Sagittarius is the **best listener** of all the star signs. It's no wonder her friends love her so much, and aren't afraid to show it.

Finding out about the world is what makes this Sagittarius tick.

SAY IT LOUD

NO ONE SAYS IT QUITE LIKE L.O.L. HERE ARE 5 OF OUR FAVOURITE SLOGANS.

We **dare** you to try dropping these into conversation! **Tick** each one off when you've spoken it.

Score them from 1 to 5! 5 is the best and 1 the worst!

CHILL OUT AND BOOGIE DOWN

/5

WHEN I'M WITH MY CREW WE FLASHY

/5

I know I'm always right

/5

LOLVILLE

/5

GLITTER GLAM 4 LYFE

© MGA

/5

Write your most favourite L.O.L. Surprise saying EVA, here!

75

ANSWERS

Page 8

Crossword answers:
1. GAME
2. BLING
3. MERRY
4. TREE
5. RESOLUTION
6. CHILL
7. SURPRISE
8. SLEIGH
9. HOLIDAYS
10. LIGHT
11. SNOW

Page 26

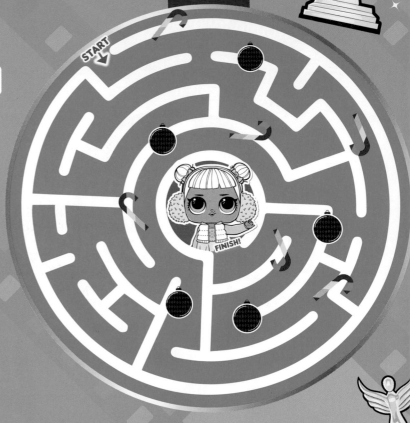

START

FINISH!

Pages 9

Page 28-29

Decks Double Up!: B and E match

Page 10

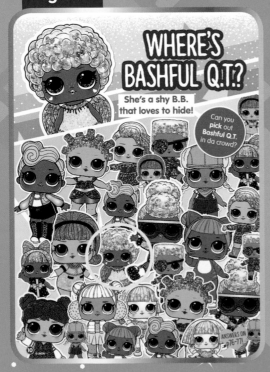

WHERE'S BASHFUL Q.T.?

She's a shy B.B. that loves to hide!

Can you pick out Bashful Q.T. in da crowd?

ANSWERS ON P76-77!

Page 44-45

Snowy Sudoku

#Fab: possible words include it, now, wet, went, cone, toe, nicer, snow, disc, write, directions.

Ice Ice Baby

1   7

Page 64

Y Y H L T I E E W O L G
B R O U S E D L A C J H
G R L L S E A S O N C R
F E I L I O V I T S L I
I M D A I O G V L U N S D
E E A Y H F T N R C P O S
R L F C R X P I A R L U
C E I S O O R U R L E C O
E Y N I B I H K S I B I J
Y E N S D L O G T C I Q
E U E M E J H H U H B W

Page 66-67

A-3. B-1. C-2.

In Bits